templar publishing

I'm going to the beach.
I've got my goggles and snorkel,

my bucket
and spade,

my flippers,

my trunks…

and my big yellow float.

All I need now is…

an aeroplane...

a sailing boat...

a truck…

a camel...

some sand...

the sea...

and a friend.

Then, when it's time to go home again…

I'll need a **tanker**...

a helicopter…

a bicycle…

and a tractor.

Home.

So now where?

A TEMPLAR BOOK

First published in the UK in 2007 by Templar Publishing,
This softback edition published in 2014 by Templar Publishing,
an imprint of The Templar Company Limited,
Deepdene Lodge, Deepdene Avenue, Dorking, Surrey, RH5 4AT, UK
www.templarco.co.uk

First softback edition, third impression

ISBN 978-1-84011-148-4

Printed in China

TO THE BEACH